# Trooper at the Beverly Hills Hotel

Written by
Susan McCauley

Illustrated by
Darlee Orcullo Urbiztondo

Celtic Sea Publishing

For Trooper,
the greatest dog who
ever lived.

Celtic Sea Publishing

Celtic Sea, LLC

6046 FM 2920, Suite 713

Spring, TX 77379

Visit our website at www.celticseallc.com

Hardcover ISBN: 978-1-951069-23-0

Paperback ISBN: 978-1-951069-22-3

eBook ISBN: 978-1-951069-21-6

Trooper loved the wide-open spaces of his Montana home. He loved chasing horses and other dogs. He loved, loved, loved rolling in the snow. And even more than that, he LOVED his best friend, Andrea Eastman.

One day Trooper found out Andrea was sick. She needed heart surgery, and the best doctors for her were in Los Angeles. But there was a problem.

Trooper hated airplanes. He'd only flown once, and the memory made him quiver. But she needs me, he thought. So, with a brave bark and a nuzzle to Andrea's knee, Trooper followed her out into the crisp autumn air and onto the tarmac where the plane was waiting.

But it wasn't just any plane. This was a shiny, special plane. Trooper heard Andrea say that her friend, Sylvester Stallone, had sent it just for them. His tail thumped, beating a happy rhythm against the ground. He was going on a private jet!

But what about his animal friends? And the wide-open spaces? And the snow? What about his home?

Well, if this is what Andrea needed to do to get better, then Trooper would be brave and stay right by her side.

A few hours later, Trooper jolted
awake as the airplane landed. When
the cabin door opened, Andrea led him
into the warm Los Angeles sunshine.

Waiting for them on the tarmac was a long limousine. Was it safe to get in that big white car? And where would it take them? Trooper wagged his tail anxiously, hoping he'd make friends in this strange new place.

12

Andrea didn't seem worried, so Trooper followed her into the biggest car he'd ever seen.

Trooper sniffed at the cool leather seats and the sparkling glasses and the brilliant blue lights.

Certain they were safe, Trooper curled up
by Andrea's feet. But before he could settle
in for a nap, the limousine stopped, and a
valet opened the door.

Outside the car was a beautiful hotel with pale pink columns, and a white-and-green striped ceiling, and a wide red carpet that led to the front doors. This place looked amazing. Now Trooper needed to meet some friends. So, holding his leash in his mouth, he leapt out of the car.

The Beverly Hills

The Beverly Hills

The Beverly Hills

He dropped the leash at the valet's feet and eagerly licked the man's hand. "Welcome to the Beverly Hills Hotel," the smiling man said. Wow! Trooper thought. So many movie stars have stayed here. Maybe I'll see one!

17

The hotel manager, Steven Boggs, greeted Andrea and Trooper in the lobby. Trooper liked the shimmering lights and colorful flowers and creamy sofas. Maybe he could take a nap on one?

But he didn't have time to try a sofa. Keys in hand, Steven led
Trooper and Andrea down a hallway with lots and lots of doors.
Finally, they stopped at one of the doors and went inside.

The Beverly Hills Hotel

The room had soft carpet, comfy-looking sofas, and a great, big bed! Trooper pranced toward the bed. Maybe he could bounce on it! But he stopped when he spotted something on the floor. Was that for him? He sniffed. Then sniffed again. It smelled friendly. But how did it feel?

Trooper leapt onto his very own super soft, comfy-cozy bed. Maybe he could bounce on this one. . . . Then he saw something even more exciting. A bone-shaped doggie treat with his name on it! "Room service," Andrea called it.

Dinner in your bedroom! This place was great! If he kept getting treats and meeting people as nice as Steven and the valet, he would definitely be happy here. He just hoped his Andrea would be okay when she had her surgery.

Thankfully, Andrea's surgery went very well. Kind people helped her every day, and every day Trooper would prance down the hallway and greet the hotel staff behind the front desk. "Good morning, Trooper!" they'd say, and he'd wag his tail, looking forward to his walk.

They took him to the pool, where a man named Alec gave him icy water to drink and a cool pad to lie on. Trooper played hide-the-cap with the gardener. He met so many nice people—even some movie stars!

But his best friend at the hotel was Renato. Every day, Renato took Trooper to explore. There was even an area of lush green grass to roll around on.

Renato always said, "You're such a good boy, Trooper." And Trooper was a good boy. He was making friends and taking care of his Andrea.

Trooper was there as Andrea got stronger and stronger, and soon she could walk Trooper like before. Andrea was almost well.

Then one day, Trooper saw Andrea packing her suitcase, and he knew they were going home. He was a little sad. He wanted to go back to his home in Montana, but he was going to miss this place and all his new friends.

"It's okay, Trooper," Andrea said, hugging him. "We will come back to visit."

27

Trooper was happy to be back in Montana. Andrea was healthy again, and he enjoyed playing with his old friends. But as he sat gazing out at the spring sunset, he realized something that made his heart soar: Whether he was here in Montana with Andrea or with her at the Beverly Hills Hotel, he had friends. And wherever he had friends, he would always be home.

# About Andrea Eastman and Trooper

Andrea Eastman began her career at Paramount Pictures and was the casting director for *Love Story* (1970) and *The Godfather* (1972). She later worked as Senior VP at International Creative Management (ICM), where she represented many clients including Sylvester Stallone, Barbra Streisand, Gabriel Byrne, Billy Crystal, Dustin Hoffman, Marshall Brickman, Richard Gere, Chevy Chase, Stockard Channing, Wes Craven, Christopher Plummer, Katharine Ross, Paul Michael Glaser, Tony Danza, Katie Couric, James Brolin, Roy Scheider, and Henry Winkler.

She moved to Montana in 2005, where she embraced her lifelong love of animals and has worked extensively in horse advocacy. As an animal activist, she has supported rescue groups worldwide to protect and improve the lives of animals. In 2021, Andrea Eastman and Willie Nelson received a lifetime achievement award from Equine Advocates for horse rescue.

Andrea went to Los Angeles for open heart surgery in 2020. During her time there, she lived at the Beverly Hills Hotel for three months. Trooper, her beloved golden retriever, was with her the entire time and was a huge part of helping her heal. Andrea had a special bond with Trooper. He walked step-by-step with her when she first began walking after surgery; she's not sure how she would have gotten through it without him. Trooper was the most sensitive, loving, and intelligent dog she could have hoped for. She loved him so very much. Sadly, Trooper passed away in January 2022. He was thirteen years old.

Andrea is thankful for the support of so many of her family and friends. She is especially thankful to her dear friend Sylvester Stallone, who not only visited her while she recovered, but who also sent a plane to take her and Trooper to Los Angeles (and home again). Andrea would also like to thank Barbra Streisand for arranging her care at the Barbra Streisand Women's Heart Center at Cedars-Sinai in Los Angeles. Andrea appreciates all of her wonderful friends who visited her while she recuperated. She's also extremely grateful to Steven Boggs, Mitchell Armstrong and all the concierge staff, Alec Foster, Chef Sebastien Guillemin, Renato Tayson, as well as to her caregivers, especially Mary Adeyemo, housekeeper Maria Valle, and the entire Beverly Hills Hotel staff who welcomed her and Trooper and made them feel at home.

Trooper at home in Montana.

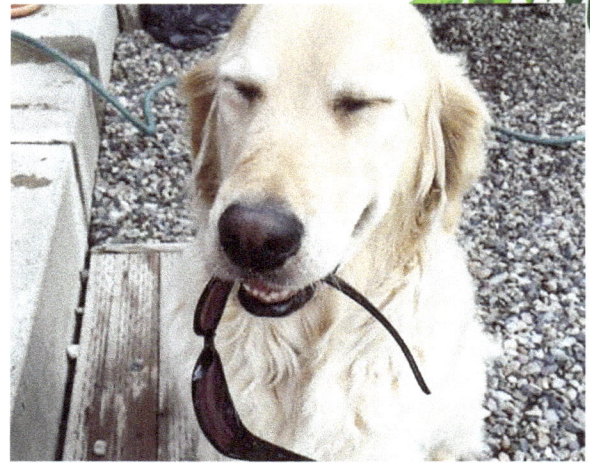

Aside from his leash, Trooper loved to snatch things and carry them around.

Andrea and Trooper enjoying a horseback ride in the Montana snow.

Andrea and Trooper out for a walk in the snow.

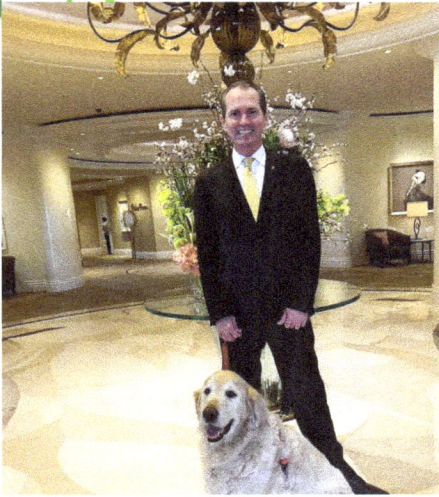

Concierge Mitchell Armstrong and Trooper in the lobby of the Beverly Hills Hotel.

Steven Boggs, Director of Global Guest Relations, at the Beverly Hills Hotel.

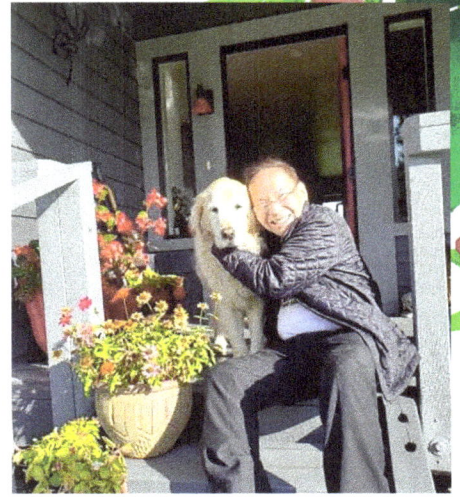

Renato Tayson and Trooper in Montana.

Andrea and Trooper in Sly Stallone's jet on the way to Los Angeles.

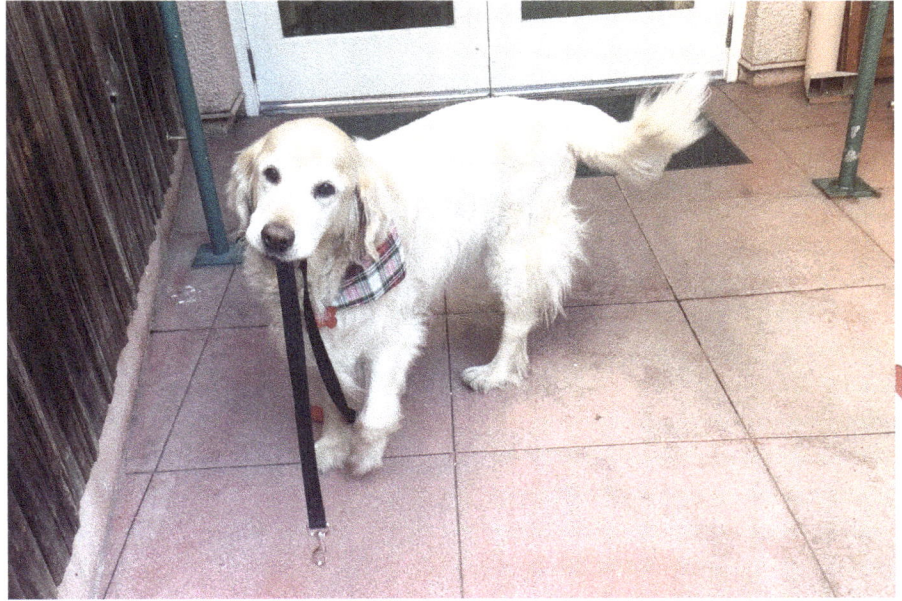

Trooper carrying his leash at the Beverly Hills Hotel.

# ABOUT THE AUTHOR

Susan McCauley is an award-winning author of both children and adult books. She received a B.A. from the University of Houston, an M.F.A. in writing from the University of Southern California, and an M.A. in Text & Performance at the Royal Academy of Dramatic Art and King's College London. She studied acting at Playhouse West with Robert Carnegie and Jeff Goldblum. Susan has lived on all three coasts of the United States and spent a few years living in London, England. She loves to travel, snorkel and scuba dive, practice Taekwondo (she's a black belt), read, watch movies, and go to the theatre. She is passionate about animals and has a special place in her heart for cats.

If you'd like to learn more, please visit her at www.sbmccauley.com.

# ABOUT THE ILLUSTRATOR

Darlee Urbiztondo, also known as Happylee, is a multi-disciplinary Filipino creative based in the Philippines. She loves digital illustrations, painting, calligraphy, graphic design, and traditional art. She believes that art is an extension of her soul, and she strives to learn new things and to keep improving her work. By creating magical and whimsical pieces, she creates happiness for herself and hopes to impart this happiness to readers. Darlee enjoys a good cup of coffee, books, movies, TV shows, anime, and singing.

If you'd like to learn more, please visit her at www.thehappylee.com.

# ACKNOWLEDGEMENTS

I'd like to thank Andrea Eastman for giving me the opportunity to share this sweet story about her and Trooper and their time at the Beverly Hills Hotel. It's been a privilege to get to know Andrea, to learn about her wonderful Trooper, and to better acquaint myself with the people and history of the iconic Beverly Hills Hotel. I'd also like to thank David Baxter for introducing me to Andrea.

Finally, a special thanks to Pat Cuchens, Deborah Halverson, Shannon Kelly, and Katie Lopez for their input and support for this book. And, as always, thank you to my mother, Sandy Basso, and to my husband, Rick McCauley, and my son, Alex McCauley, for their unending love and support.

"Some of my best leading men have been dogs and horses."

—Elizabeth Taylor

www.ingramcontent.com/pod-product-compliance
Lightning Source LLC
Chambersburg PA
CBHW042147240326
41723CB00014B/613

9 781951 069230